LIFE, WITHOUT YOU 978-1-9999965-1-2

First published in Great Britain by Ultimate Publications
This edition published 2018
Text copyright © Kelly Owen, 2018
Illustrations copyright © Helen Braid, 2018

The right of Kelly Owen and Helen Braid to be identified
as the author and illustrator of this work has been asserted in
accordance with the Copyright, Designs and Patents Act 1988.

All rights reserved. No part of this publication may be reproduced,
stored in a retrieval system, or transmitted in any form or by any
means, electronic, mechanical, photocopying, recording or otherwise,
without the prior permission of the publisher.

www.chasingdragonfliesblog.com
Ultimate Publications is a trading name of Ultimate Proof Ltd.
Reg no. 07720107

A CIP catalogue record for this book is available from the British Library.
Printed in the UK by Acorn Press Ltd, Swindon.

Dear friend,

If you have bought this book for yourself or have been gifted it, then I'm sorry.

I'm so sorry you are grieving.

It is my hope, by creating this journal, that you can find some comfort in recognizing how you feel day to day, offloading some of those thoughts crowding your mind.

There is much about grief that you can share online if you choose; however, this journal is a private space for you to note down whatever you want - it might be the anger that you can't speak, the fearful, anxious thoughts, or the gratitude in the small things you notice around you.

There are different sections of the journal, and each has been carefully illustrated to guide you gently to record your thoughts.

There are also spaces to simply pause and colour in, when you can't seem to work out what you're feeling. You can write as much or as little as you feel. Over time, you might notice a change in your emotions, the tears not falling quite so often or you may have smiled at a memory…

Allow yourself to travel with your grief, it's now a part of you, just like your loved one was… the path to adjustment is not easy, but it is possible.

If you have any suggestions for this journal or would like to know more, please contact me via my website: www.chasingdragonfliesblog.com

With love,
Kelly x

CHASING DRAGONFLIES

Contents of your journal...

Journalling Tips

Keeping a journal can be a useful way to reflect and better understand who you are and what is important to you. When you find yourself in the midst of a personal loss, journalling can help you express how you are feeling in a safe and private way. This journal will not change your loss, but it might show you how you have changed, and how you can use that knowledge as part of your healing.

Every loss is a personal experience, and this journal has been carefully presented to help guide you through some of the common areas that grief impacts. The 'My Days Without You' diary pages have been designed to focus your mind and give you a way to capture your thoughts and feelings. Towards the back of the journal are pages dedicated to remembering your lost loved one and the early memories surrounding their death and funeral, as well as aspects such as their favourite things and signs or things that remind you of them. You can complete these sections first if you wish, or complete them much later than the main journal, or not use them at all.

Start when you are ready

If you bought this journal for yourself then you might want to start straight away; however, if it was a gift, don't feel you have to start until you are ready. This journal can be used at any time and can help you through some key periods such as during the early weeks of bereavement, while waiting for therapy, before returning to work, etc.

Seek help

A journal is a 'mind space', it is not there to judge, give advice or criticize. If you feel unable to cope, or are experiencing deep trauma or distress, seek help from professional grief therapists, your GP and loved ones. Do not try to cope alone. Early grief in particular can be frightening, and while it must be allowed to happen, you don't need to go through it on your own.

It's okay that you might not be able to do things you used to do. It's often the day-to-day mundane tasks, such as shopping, that are hardest to face. It might feel silly writing that all you managed to do that day was get up and have a shower, but it's noting these small steps that will, in time, help you see progress and also where you need more support.

Connect every day

There are 100 diary pages for you to use over approximately 3 months. Try to complete a diary spread every day, in the evening or bedtime is best. It's important to add a date to your entry, so that you can look back and review how you are doing.

Buy yourself a nice pen and some colouring pencils just for use in this journal. If you wish, use the spaces in the diary to doodle or write key words on your mind. Or, colour in the small illustrations on the pages to help you relax.

The diary pages offer prompts and questions for you to complete, so you don't have to think about what to say. It doesn't matter if you fill pages with the same thoughts, or if you find it impossible to think of any 'good things' to write down, keep going, at some point you might begin to notice a shift in your feelings.

Little and often

You don't have to spend too much time completing the pages, about 10-15 minutes is plenty. Your mind may be foggy with grief and concentrating for too long can be tiring. You can do your daily entry in one sitting or carry it with you to complete during the day as thoughts arise.

If you're not feeling able to write much on a day, complete what you can and try to capture three things you are grateful for. It may be tiny things such as someone making you a cup of tea, or a text a friend sent you; small things matter.

Reflect and review

When you have finished a day's entry, read it back to yourself with love and self-compassion. Our thoughts look different when they are written down. To see that there have been some better moments among the pain and grief can help bring a clearer picture of your loss and where you find your comfort. There are review spreads inserted after around 30 days of journaling to help you take stock of what's helped you get through the weeks.

Remember, this journal hasn't been created to help you get over your loss, but it will help you on your journey through it.

"But in all of the sadness when you're feeling that your heart is empty, and lacking, you've got to remember that grief isn't the absence of love. Grief is the proof that love is still there."

★ TESSA SHAFFER. HEAVEN HAS NO REGRETS

My Days Without You

This is your journal so use it how you like.
The prompts are there to guide your
thoughts to consider how you are feeling
and what is most on your mind. There are
also areas to help bring those small but
significant healing steps into focus.

Remember, healing doesn't mean forgetting,
it's about finding a way to live on without
your loved one in your own way.

What I did today

- ....
- ....
- ....
- ....
- ....

Date:

Grief trigger

....
....

Today's kind word

Colour of my emotions

What did I notice today?

3 special things

- ....
- ....
- ....

Self-care

- ....
- ....
- ....

What I did today

* ....
* ....
* ....
* ....
* ....

Grief trigger

....
....

Date:

Today's kind word

Colour of my emotions

What did I notice today?

3 special things

🐞 ....
🐞 ....
🐞 ....

Self-care

☕ ....
☕ ....
☕ ....

What I did today

- ....
- ....
- ....
- ....
- ....

Date:

Grief trigger

....
....

Today's kind word

Colour of my emotions

What did I notice today?

3 special things

- ....
- ....
- ....

Self-care

....
....
....

What I did today

- ....
- ....
- ....
- ....
- ....

Date:

Grief trigger

....
....
....

Today's kind word

Colour of my emotions

What did I notice today?

3 special things

....
....
....

Self-care

....
....
....

What I did today

- ....
- ....
- ....
- ....
- ....

Grief trigger

....
....

Date:

Today's kind word

Colour of my emotions

What did I notice today?

3 special things

- ....
- ....
- ....

Self-care

- ....
- ....
- ....

What I did today

Date:

- ....
- ....
- ....
- ....
- ....

Grief trigger

....
....

Today's kind word

Colour of my emotions

What did I notice today?

3 special things

....
....
....

Self-care

....
....
....

What I did today

- ....
- ....
- ....
- ....
- ....

Date:

Grief trigger

....
....

Today's kind word

Colour of my emotions

What did I notice today?

3 special things

....
....
....

Self-care

....
....
....

What I did today

*

*

*

*

*

Date:

Grief trigger

Today's kind word

What did I notice today?

Colour of my emotions

3 special things

Self-care

What I did today

Date:

- ....
- ....
- ....
- ....
- ....

Grief trigger

....
....

Today's kind word

Colour of my emotions

What did I notice today?

3 special things

- ....
- ....
- ....

Self-care

- ....
- ....
- ....

What I did today

- ....
- ....
- ....
- ....
- ....

Date:

Grief trigger

....
....

Today's kind word

Colour of my emotions

What did I notice today?

3 special things

....
....
....

Self-care

....
....
....

What I did today

- ....
- ....
- ....
- ....
- ....

Date:

Grief trigger

....
....

Today's kind word

Colour of my emotions

What did I notice today?

3 special things

- ....
- ....
- ....

Self-care

- ....
- ....
- ....

What I did today

- ....
- ....
- ....
- ....
- ....

Date:

Grief trigger

....
....

Today's kind word

Colour of my emotions

What did I notice today?

3 special things

- ....
- ....
- ....

Self-care

- ....
- ....
- ....

What I did today

Date:

- ....
- ....
- ....
- ....
- ....

Grief trigger

....
....

Today's kind word

Colour of my emotions

What did I notice today?

3 special things

- ....
- ....
- ....

Self-care

....
....
....

What I did today

- ....
- ....
- ....
- ....
- ....

Date:

Grief trigger

....
....

Today's kind word

Colour of my emotions

What did I notice today?

3 special things

....

....

....

Self-care

....

....

....

What I did today

- ....
- ....
- ....
- ....
- ....

Date:

Grief trigger

....
....
....

Today's kind word

Colour of my emotions

What did I notice today?

3 special things

- ....
- ....
- ....

Self-care

- ....
- ....
- ....

What I did today

Date

- ....
- ....
- ....
- ....
- ....

Grief trigger

....

....

Today's kind word

Colour of my emotions

What did I notice today?

3 special things

- ....
- ....
- ....

Self-care

- ....
- ....
- ....

What I did today

Date:

- ....
- ....
- ....
- ....
- ....

Grief trigger

....
....

Today's kind word

Colour of my emotions

What did I notice today?

3 special things

....
....
....

Self-care

....
....
....

What I did today

- ....
- ....
- ....
- ....
- ....

Date:

Grief trigger

....

....

Today's kind word

What did I notice today?

Colour of my emotions

3 special things

....

....

....

Self-care

....

....

....

What I did today

Date:

- ....
- ....
- ....
- ....
- ....

Grief trigger

....
....

Colour of my emotions

Today's kind word

What did I notice today?

3 special things

....
....
....

Self-care

....
....
....

What I did today

Date:

- ....
- ....
- ....
- ....
- ....

Grief trigger

....

....

Today's kind word

Colour of my emotions

What did I notice today?

3 special things

- ....
- ....
- ....

Self-care

- ....
- ....
- ....

What I did today

Date:

- ....
- ....
- ....
- ....
- ....

Grief trigger

....

....

Today's kind word

Colour of my emotions

What did I notice today?

3 special things

- ....
- ....
- ....

Self-care

- ....
- ....
- ....

What I did today

Date:

- ....
- ....
- ....
- ....
- ....

Grief trigger

....
....
....

Today's kind word

Colour of my emotions

What did I notice today?

3 special things

- ....
- ....
- ....

Self-care

- ....
- ....
- ....

What I did today

- ....
- ....
- ....
- ....
- ....

Grief trigger

....
....

Date:

Today's kind word

Colour of my emotions

What did I notice today?

3 special things

- ....
- ....
- ....

Self-care

....
....
....

What I did today

- ....
- ....
- ....
- ....
- ....

Grief trigger

....
....

Date:

Today's kind word

What did I notice today?

Colour of my emotions

3 special things

🐞 ....

🐞 ....

🐞 ....

Self-care

☕ ....

☕ ....

☕ ....

What I did today

Date:

- ....
- ....
- ....
- ....
- ....

Grief trigger

....
....

Today's kind word

Colour of my emotions

What did I notice today?

3 special things

- ....
- ....
- ....

Self-care

- ....
- ....
- ....

What I did today

Date:

- ....
- ....
- ....
- ....
- ....

Grief trigger

....
....

Today's kind word

Colour of my emotions

What did I notice today?

3 special things

....
....
....

Self-care

....
....
....

What I did today

- ....
- ....
- ....
- ....
- ....

Date:

Grief trigger

....

....

Today's kind word

Colour of my emotions

What did I notice today?

3 special things

- ....
- ....
- ....

Self-care

- ....
- ....
- ....

What I did today

Date:

- ....
- ....
- ....
- ....
- ....

Grief trigger

Today's kind word

....
....
....

What did I notice today?

Colour of my emotions

3 special things

....
....
....

Self-care

....
....
....

What I did today

- ....
- ....
- ....
- ....
- ....

Date:

Grief trigger

....
....

Today's kind word

Colour of my emotions

What did I notice today?

3 special things

....
....
....

Self-care

....
....
....

What I did today

Date:

- ....
- ....
- ....
- ....
- ....

Grief trigger

....
....
....

Today's kind word

Colour of my emotions

What did I notice today?

3 special things

....
....
....

Self-care

....
....
....

What I did today

Date:

- ....
- ....
- ....
- ....
- ....

Grief trigger

....
....

Today's kind word

Colour of my emotions

What did I notice today?

3 special things

- ....
- ....
- ....

Self-care

- ....
- ....
- ....

What I did today

- ....
- ....
- ....
- ....
- ....

Grief trigger

....
....

Date:

Today's kind word

Colour of my emotions

What did I notice today?

3 special things

....
....
....

Self-care

....
....
....

What I did today

- ....
- ....
- ....
- ....
- ....

Date.

Grief trigger

....
....

Today's kind word

Colour of my emotions

What did I notice today?

3 special things

....
....
....

Self-care

....
....
....

What I did today

- ....
- ....
- ....
- ....
- ....

Date:

Grief trigger

....
....

Today's kind word

Colour of my emotions

What did I notice today?

3 special things

....
....
....

Self-care

....
....
....

Review

Has my grief changed? If so, how?

Words to describe me

Five things I'm grateful for

- ....
- ....
- ....
- ....
- ....

What positive steps have I taken to care for myself?

Where do I feel most peaceful?

Which people do I need?

What I did today

Date:

- ....
- ....
- ....
- ....
- ....

Grief trigger

....
....

Today's kind word

Colour of my emotions

What did I notice today?

3 special things

- ....
- ....
- ....

Self-care

- ....
- ....
- ....

What I did today

- ....
- ....
- ....
- ....
- ....

Date:

Grief trigger

....
....

Today's kind word

Colour of my emotions

What did I notice today?

3 special things

- ....
- ....
- ....

Self-care

- ....
- ....
- ....

What I did today

Date:

- ....
- ....
- ....
- ....
- ....

Grief trigger

....

....

Today's kind word

Colour of my emotions

What did I notice today?

3 special things

- ....
- ....
- ....

Self-care

- ....
- ....
- ....

What I did today

- ....
- ....
- ....
- ....
- ....

Date:

Grief trigger

....
....

Today's kind word

Colour of my emotions

What did I notice today?

3 special things

....
....
....

Self-care

....
....
....

What I did today

Date:

- ....
- ....
- ....
- ....
- ....

Grief trigger

....
....

Today's kind word

Colour of my emotions

What did I notice today?

3 special things

- ....
- ....
- ....

Self-care

....
....
....

What I did today

- ....
- ....
- ....
- ....
- ....

Grief trigger

....
....

Date:

Today's kind word

Colour of my emotions

What did I notice today?

3 special things

- ....
- ....
- ....

Self-care

....
....
....

What I did today

Date.

- ....
- ....
- ....
- ....
- ....

Grief trigger

....
....

Colour of my emotions

Today's kind word

What did I notice today?

3 special things

- ....
- ....
- ....

Self-care

- ....
- ....
- ....

What I did today

Date:

- ....
- ....
- ....
- ....
- ....

Grief trigger

....

....

Today's kind word

Colour of my emotions

What did I notice today?

3 special things

- ....
- ....
- ....

Self-care

- ....
- ....
- ....

What I did today

* ....
* ....
* ....
* ....
* ....

Date:

Grief trigger

....
....

Today's kind word

Colour of my emotions

What did I notice today?

3 special things

....
....
....

Self-care

....
....
....

What I did today

- ....
- ....
- ....
- ....
- ....

Date:

Grief trigger

....

....

Today's kind word

Colour of my emotions

What did I notice today?

3 special things

....
....
....

Self-care

....
....
....

What I did today

Date:

- ....
- ....
- ....
- ....
- ....

Grief trigger

....

....

Today's kind word

Colour of my emotions

What did I notice today?

3 special things

- ....
- ....
- ....

Self-care

- ....
- ....
- ....

What I did today

- ....
- ....
- ....
- ....
- ....

Grief trigger

....
....

Date:

Today's kind word

Colour of my emotions

What did I notice today?

3 special things

....
....
....

Self-care

....
....
....

What I did today

- ....
- ....
- ....
- ....
- ....

Date:

Grief trigger

....

....

Today's kind word

Colour of my emotions

What did I notice today?

3 special things

- ....
- ....
- ....

Self-care

- ....
- ....
- ....

What I did today

Date:

- ....
- ....
- ....
- ....
- ....

Grief trigger

....
....

Today's kind word

Colour of my emotions

What did I notice today?

3 special things

....
....
....

Self-care

....
....
....

What I did today

Date:

- ....
- ....
- ....
- ....
- ....

Grief trigger

....

....

Today's kind word

Colour of my emotions

What did I notice today?

3 special things

- ....
- ....
- ....

Self-care

- ....
- ....
- ....

What I did today

- ....
- ....
- ....
- ....
- ....

Grief trigger

....

....

Date:

Today's kind word

Colour of my emotions

What did I notice today?

3 special things

....

....

....

Self-care

....

....

....

What I did today

Date:

- ....
- ....
- ....
- ....
- ....

Grief trigger

....

....

Today's kind word

Colour of my emotions

What did I notice today?

3 special things

- ....
- ....
- ....

Self-care

- ....
- ....
- ....

What I did today

- ....
- ....
- ....
- ....
- ....

Date:

Grief trigger

....
....

Today's kind word

Colour of my emotions

What did I notice today?

3 special things

- ....
- ....
- ....

Self-care

- ....
- ....
- ....

What I did today

Date.

- ....
- ....
- ....
- ....
- ....

Grief trigger

....

....

Today's kind word

Colour of my emotions

What did I notice today?

3 special things

- ....
- ....
- ....

Self-care

- ....
- ....
- ....

What I did today

Date:

- ....
- ....
- ....
- ....
- ....

Grief trigger

....

....

Today's kind word

Colour of my emotions

What did I notice today?

3 special things

- ....
- ....
- ....

Self-care

- ....
- ....
- ....

What I did today

Date:

- ....
- ....
- ....
- ....
- ....

Grief trigger

....

....

Today's kind word

Colour of my emotions

What did I notice today?

3 special things

- ....
- ....
- ....

Self-care

- ....
- ....
- ....

What I did today

- ....
- ....
- ....
- ....
- ....

Grief trigger

....

....

Colour of my emotions

Today's kind word

What did I notice today?

3 special things

- ....
- ....
- ....

Self-care

- ....
- ....
- ....

Date:

What I did today

Date:

- ....
- ....
- ....
- ....
- ....

Grief trigger

....
....

Today's kind word

Colour of my emotions

What did I notice today?

3 special things

- ....
- ....
- ....

Self-care

- ....
- ....
- ....

What I did today

- ....
- ....
- ....
- ....
- ....

Date:

Grief trigger

....
....

Today's kind word

Colour of my emotions

What did I notice today?

3 special things

....
....
....

Self-care

....
....
....

What I did today

- ....
- ....
- ....
- ....
- ....

Date:

Grief trigger

....

....

Today's kind word

Colour of my emotions

What did I notice today?

3 special things

....

....

....

Self-care

....

....

....

What I did today

- ....
- ....
- ....
- ....
- ....

Date:

Grief trigger

....

....

Today's kind word

Colour of my emotions

What did I notice today?

3 special things

....

....

....

Self-care

....

....

....

What I did today

Date:

- ....
- ....
- ....
- ....
- ....

Grief trigger

....

....

Today's kind word

Colour of my emotions

What did I notice today?

3 special things

- ....
- ....
- ....

Self-care

- ....
- ....
- ....

What I did today

- ....
- ....
- ....
- ....
- ....

Date:

Grief trigger

....
....

Today's kind word

What did I notice today?

Colour of my emotions

3 special things

....
....
....

Self-care

....
....
....

What I did today

Date:

- ....
- ....
- ....
- ....
- ....

Grief trigger

....
....

Today's kind word

Colour of my emotions

What did I notice today?

3 special things

- ....
- ....
- ....

Self-care

- ....
- ....
- ....

What I did today

Date:

- ....
- ....
- ....
- ....
- ....

Grief trigger

....
....

Today's kind word

Colour of my emotions

What did I notice today?

3 special things

....

....

....

Self-care

....

....

....

73

What I did today

- ....
- ....
- ....
- ....
- ....

Grief trigger

....
....

Date:

Today's kind word

Colour of my emotions

What did I notice today?

3 special things

....
....
....

Self-care

....
....
....

What I did today

Date:

- ....
- ....
- ....
- ....
- ....

Grief trigger

....

....

Today's kind word

Colour of my emotions

What did I notice today?

3 special things

....

....

....

Self-care

....

....

....

Review

Has my grief changed? If so, how?

★ ♥ ★

Words to describe me

Five things I'm grateful for

- ....
- ....
- ....
- ....
- ....

What positive steps have I taken to care for myself?

Where do I feel most peaceful?

Which people do I need?

What I did today

Date:

- ....
- ....
- ....
- ....
- ....

Grief trigger

....
....

Today's kind word

Colour of my emotions

What did I notice today?

3 special things

- ....
- ....
- ....

Self-care

- ....
- ....
- ....

What I did today

*   ....
*   ....
*   ....
*   ....
*   ....

Date:

Grief trigger

....
....

Today's kind word

Colour of my emotions

What did I notice today?

3 special things

....
....
....

Self-care

....
....
....

What I did today

- ....
- ....
- ....
- ....
- ....

Date:

Grief trigger

....

....

Today's kind word

Colour of my emotions

What did I notice today?

3 special things

- ....
- ....
- ....

Self-care

- ....
- ....
- ....

What I did today

Date:

- ....
- ....
- ....
- ....
- ....

Grief trigger

....

....

Today's kind word

Colour of my emotions

What did I notice today?

3 special things

- ....
- ....
- ....

Self-care

- ....
- ....
- ....

What I did today

- ....
- ....
- ....
- ....
- ....

Date:

Grief trigger

....
....

Today's kind word

Colour of my emotions

What did I notice today?

3 special things

🐞 ....
🐞 ....
🐞 ....

Self-care

☕ ....
☕ ....
☕ ....

What I did today

- ....
- ....
- ....
- ....
- ....

Date:

Grief trigger

....
....

Today's kind word

Colour of my emotions

What did I notice today?

3 special things

....
....
....

Self-care

....
....
....

What I did today

Date:

- ....
- ....
- ....
- ....
- ....

Grief trigger

....

....

Today's kind word

Colour of my emotions

What did I notice today?

3 special things

....

....

....

Self-care

....

....

....

What I did today

Date:

- ....
- ....
- ....
- ....
- ....

Grief trigger

....

....

Today's kind word

Colour of my emotions

What did I notice today?

3 special things

- ....
- ....
- ....

Self-care

- ....
- ....
- ....

What I did today

- ....
- ....
- ....
- ....
- ....

Date:

Grief trigger

....

....

Today's kind word

Colour of my emotions

What did I notice today?

3 special things

....

....

....

Self-care

....

....

....

What I did today

Date:

- ....
- ....
- ....
- ....
- ....

Grief trigger

....

....

Today's kind word

Colour of my emotions

What did I notice today?

3 special things

- ....
- ....
- ....

Self-care

- ....
- ....
- ....

What I did today

Date:

- ....
- ....
- ....
- ....
- ....

Grief trigger

....

....

Today's kind word

What did I notice today?

Colour of my emotions

3 special things

- ....
- ....
- ....

Self-care

- ....
- ....
- ....

What I did today

- ....
- ....
- ....
- ....
- ....

Date:

Grief trigger

....

....

Today's kind word

Colour of my emotions

What did I notice today?

3 special things

- ....
- ....
- ....

Self-care

- ....
- ....
- ....

What I did today

Date:

- ....
- ....
- ....
- ....
- ....

Grief trigger

....

....

Today's kind word

Colour of my emotions

What did I notice today?

3 special things

....
....
....

Self-care

....
....
....

What I did today

- ....
- ....
- ....
- ....
- ....

Grief trigger

....
....

Date:

Today's kind word

Colour of my emotions

What did I notice today?

3 special things

- ....
- ....
- ....

Self-care

- ....
- ....
- ....

What I did today

Date.

- ....
- ....
- ....
- ....
- ....

Grief trigger

....

....

Today's kind word

Colour of my emotions

What did I notice today?

3 special things

- ....
- ....
- ....

Self-care

- ....
- ....
- ....

What I did today

Date:

- ....
- ....
- ....
- ....
- ....

Grief trigger

....

....

Today's kind word

Colour of my emotions

What did I notice today?

3 special things

- ....
- ....
- ....

Self-care

- ....
- ....
- ....

What I did today

- ....
- ....
- ....
- ....
- ....

Date:

Grief trigger

....
....

Today's kind word

Colour of my emotions

What did I notice today?

3 special things

- ....
- ....
- ....

Self-care

- ....
- ....
- ....

What I did today

- ....
- ....
- ....
- ....
- ....

Date:

Grief trigger

....
....

Today's kind word

Colour of my emotions

What did I notice today?

3 special things

- ....
- ....
- ....

Self-care

- ....
- ....
- ....

What I did today

Date:

- ....
- ....
- ....
- ....
- ....

Grief trigger

....

....

Today's kind word

Colour of my emotions

What did I notice today?

3 special things

- ....
- ....
- ....

Self-care

- ....
- ....
- ....

What I did today

- ....
- ....
- ....
- ....
- ....

Date:

Grief trigger

....
....

Today's kind word

Colour of my emotions

What did I notice today?

3 special things

....
....
....

Self-care

....
....
....

What I did today

- ....
- ....
- ....
- ....
- ....

Grief trigger

....
....
....

Date:

Today's kind word

0 0 0 0 0 0

Colour of my emotions

What did I notice today?

3 special things

....
....
....

Self-care

....
....
....

What I did today

- ....
- ....
- ....
- ....
- ....

Date:

Grief trigger

....
....

Today's kind word

What did I notice today?

Colour of my emotions

3 special things

- ....
- ....
- ....

Self-care

- ....
- ....
- ....

What I did today

Date:

- ....
- ....
- ....
- ....
- ....

Grief trigger

....

....

Today's kind word

Colour of my emotions

What did I notice today?

3 special things

- ....
- ....
- ....

Self-care

- ....
- ....
- ....

What I did today

- ....
- ....
- ....
- ....
- ....

Grief trigger

....
....

Date:

Today's kind word

Colour of my emotions

What did I notice today?

3 special things

....
....
....

Self-care

....
....
....

What I did today

Date:

- ....
- ....
- ....
- ....
- ....

Grief trigger

....

....

Today's kind word

Colour of my emotions

What did I notice today?

3 special things

- ....
- ....
- ....

Self-care

- ....
- ....
- ....

What I did today

- ....
- ....
- ....
- ....
- ....

Grief trigger

....

....

Date:

Today's kind word

Colour of my emotions

What did I notice today?

3 special things

....

....

....

Self-care

....

....

....

What I did today

Date:

- ....
- ....
- ....
- ....
- ....

Grief trigger

....

....

Today's kind word

Colour of my emotions

What did I notice today?

3 special things

- ....
- ....
- ....

Self-care

- ....
- ....
- ....

What I did today

- ....
- ....
- ....
- ....
- ....

Date:

Grief trigger

....
....

Today's kind word

Colour of my emotions

What did I notice today?

3 special things

- ....
- ....
- ....

Self-care

- ....
- ....
- ....

What I did today

- ....
- ....
- ....
- ....
-

Date:

Grief trigger

....
....

Today's kind word

Colour of my emotions

What did I notice today?

3 special things

....
....
....

Self-care

....
....
....

What I did today

Date:

- ....
- ....
- ....
- ....
- ....

Grief trigger

....
....
....

Today's kind word

Colour of my emotions

What did I notice today?

3 special things

- ....
- ....
- ....

Self-care

- ....
- ....
- ....

What I did today

Date:

- ....
- ....
- ....
- ....
- ....

Grief trigger

....

....

Today's kind word

Colour of my emotions

What did I notice today?

3 special things

- ....
- ....
- ....

Self-care

- ....
- ....
- ....

What I did today

Date:

- ....
- ....
- ....
- ....
- ....

Grief trigger

....

....

Today's kind word

Colour of my emotions

What did I notice today?

3 special things

- ....
- ....
- ....

Self-care

- ....
- ....
- ....

What I did today

Date:

- ....
- ....
- ....
- ....
- ....

Grief trigger

....
....

Today's kind word

Colour of my emotions

What did I notice today?

3 special things

- ....
- ....
- ....

Self-care

- ....
- ....
- ....

What I did today

Date:

- ....
- ....
- ....
- ....
- ....

Grief trigger

....

....

Today's kind word

Colour of my emotions

What did I notice today?

3 special things

- ....
- ....
- ....

Self-care

- ....
- ....
- ....

Review

Has my grief changed? If so, how?

Words to describe me

Five things I'm grateful for

- ....
- ....
- ....
- ....
- ....

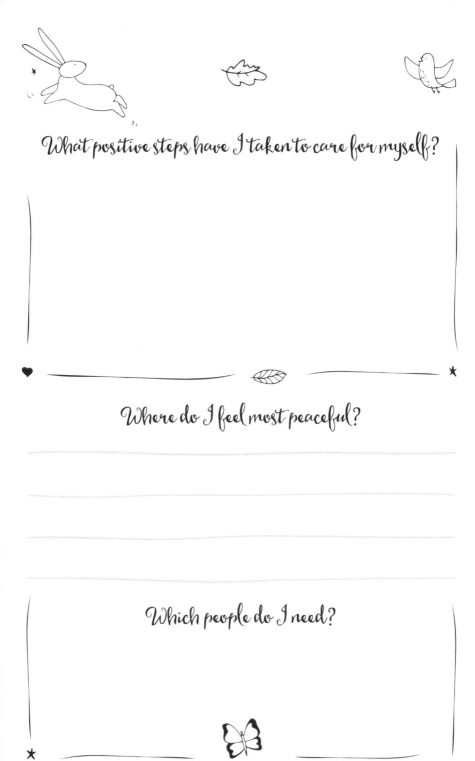

What positive steps have I taken to care for myself?

Where do I feel most peaceful?

Which people do I need?

"Grief is like the ocean,
it comes in waves, ebbing and flowing.
Sometimes, the water is calm
and sometimes it is overwhelming.
All we can do is learn to swim."

★ VICKI HARRISON

When You Left

This space is for you to record what happened. It's a free-flowing space for you to capture your memory of the time your loved one died. Writing this down may bring up strong emotions. but it is a therapeutic activity to help you to process the events surrounding your loss.

When you left

When you left

When you left

When you left

When you left

" To live in hearts we
leave behind is not to die."

★ THOMAS CAMPBELL

Saying Goodbye

The funeral of a loved one is one of the most significant moments in their life, and yours. Here, write what you remember about the funeral, making plans, the music, the place, the people... record your feelings from this day and anything that you want to remember about it.

Saying goodbye

Saying goodbye

Saying goodbye

" She was no longer wrestling with the grief,
but could sit down with it as a lasting
companion and make it a sharer
in her thoughts. "

★ GEORGE ELIOT

Here, capture the special memories of your loved one. Those things you want to remember, the little things you miss, the shared moments and what makes them so special to you. Write it as flowing text, or bullet points, draw bubbles and fill them with words or phrases, doodle and colour whatever is most natural for you...

The last time we...

Capture the many last times, last conversations,
plans for the future, holidays, times you laughed...

Your songs

What music reminds you of them? Which songs did they love?
Perhaps note down some lyrics that are special to you.

Your places

- Where did they like to be most? What were special or significant places in their life? Where did they always hope to visit?

Your favourites

What food did they love? What outfit did they always wear?
What did they love to do?

When I think of you...

Capture what you think of when you remember them,
those special moments, happy times, how they looked,
the things they said...

*"You'll always be with me,
like a handprint on my heart."*

★ ANON

Many people notice unusual or significant moments that they believe are signs from their loved one. For some, these signs are physical - a feather, a butterfly, a rainbow, a song suddenly playing. For others, they are spiritual - a feeling or sensation, a word in your mind, a sense of comfort.

Recording the signs you feel can help to build a comfort blanket as you reflect on your loved one. Turn to these pages when you most need to know they are near.

Signs of you

Signs of you

"The hard part of life is that we have to keep on living even when our world has stopped spinning, and all the stars are laying at our feet."

★ ZOE CLARK-COATES, SAYING GOODBYE

Special Days and Anniversaries

Special days take on a new meaning when you are living with loss and can be one of the hardest aspects of the year. Here, take a few moments to capture thoughts and feelings around those particular days. Record how you honoured the memory of your loved one. Reflect on how you found ways to cope. These days are hard, but they too will pass.

Special days and anniversaries

Special days and anniversaries

Special days and anniversaries

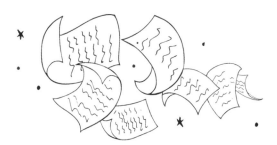

"More than kisses, letters mingle souls."

★ JOHN DONNE

Letters to You

I miss you every day

Writing letters to your lost loved one can help you to feel connected to them and is another therapeutic activity alongside journalling. Use these pages to write short letters of the things you wish you could tell them. Thank them for what they have given you. Write to them about how grief has changed you and how you plan to honour their memory in your own life. Tell them what's in your heart.

Today's date -   Writing to you from -

Dear

I love you & miss you,

Today's date -   Writing to you from -

Dear

_____

_____

_____

_____

_____

_____

_____

_____

_____

_____

_____

I love you & miss you,

★

Today's date -   Writing to you from -

Dear

I love you & miss you,

Today's date -   Writing to you from -

Dear

I love you & miss you,

Today's date -   Writing to you from -

Dear

I love you & miss you,

*

My resources

★ Notes of websites, books and anything that has helped...

When someone dies too young, too soon

When their life seems unfinished

It's as if there's only grief left

Only pain

Only the question 'Why?'

It's as though all we have trusted has deserted us

It's as though the voice of love has grown silent

The touch of love grown cold

But then, through the tears

Through the overwhelming loss

As we gently let ourselves think of them - gradually

Gradually, dawn begins to break through the darkness of night

Gradually their light, their beautiful light, begins to cast away the shadows

And there is music in the silence

Hope in the desolation

And we remember them not in sorrow only

But in a smile

In a hand held

And we can dare to believe

We can know, that death cannot separate us from all they were and are

They will always be to us our child, our friend, our self

And though we will miss them

Though we will miss them terribly in the gaping hole where they were

Yet they will bring us closer together

★ ANON